Glances at Time

A young mother's journey with breast cancer

Lisa Flaxman

ISBN 978-0-9800228-0-3

COVER IMAGE | Vase with herons by Gary Genetti, purchased by Lisa Flaxman 2005

COVER AND BOOK DESIGN | Cynthia Flaxman Frank | cfrankdesign@mindspring.com

GLANCES AT TIME is written for the patient, family, friend, child, health care provider, social worker, psychologist, psychiatrist—for everyone and anyone who has ever been affected in any way by cancer or illness, directly or indirectly.

Ms. Flaxman is available to read and discuss GLANCES AT TIME and can be contacted at lisa@musikids.com or 301.412.7516.

GLANCES AT TIME is available for $12.95 + tax. S&H is $3 per book.

25% of profits from the first printing will be donated to Georgetown Hospital Lombardi Comprehensive Center's Arts & Humanities Program under the direction of Nancy Morgan.

Table of Contents

Memories and time are strange soul mates, paired

for infinity, yet easily torn apart. Sometimes, images are

stone statues mounted on a mantle; other times, they

dance and hide, emerging from unexpected places.

We set out on a journey we think we can navigate with

confidence and yet, we always wonder where we are

going. The doubts, the questions, the fears are bound up

in the traveler's feet, moving ahead and doubling back.

Time and memory collaborate on a colorful and endless

collage, creating and destroying in the same unified

breath. –LISA FLAXMAN

This book is dedicated to my husband Jonathan, my partner, steady as the horizon; to my children, Benjamin, Sophie, and Zachary, the zest and essence of my days; to my youngest sister, Jessica Flaxman, whose courage saved my life, my hero, we walk together as one; to my sister, Cynthia Frank, who silently holds my hand and showers me with unconditional love and wisdom; to my best friend, Aviva Goldfarb, who guided me through rocky waters and always leads me to safety; to my mother and father, Rhoda and Allen Flaxman, who, in spite of living a parent's worst nightmare, refused to think of anything other than the absolute truth that I would survive; to my mother-in-law, Rhoda Martel, who died of breast cancer, the spirit of everyone breast cancer has stolen.

I am truly thankful for all the love and support I absorbed before, during, and after from my family: Pamela Bernstein, David and Alicia Flaxman, Ted, Madeline, Koby and Tessa Frank, Barbara and Mark Goldfarb, Andrew, Solomon and Celia Goldfarb, Lisa Hammer, Caryn Martel, David Martel, Susan and Jeffrey Sussman, Jake and Julia Sussman;

And for the wonderful friends who kept me going during treatments, surgeries, good days and bad: Laura Ginns, Stephanie Lowet, Kim Tilley, Elizabeth Cullen, Monica and John Rosenquist, Claudia Adas, Paola Marca, Nancy Morgan, Melissa McGraw, Tara Heery, Bob Charles, Lauren Randel, Fenella Morriss, Megan Rulli, Nadine Rubenstein, Eileen Alexander, Jen Hirshon, Madhavi Niak, Sally Pessin, Ginny Maycock, Avi Adler, Debbie Lehrich, Becky Lowenthal, Kshanila Ghandi, Ruth Schimel, and Edith Sievers.

How lucky I am to be connected to so many truly amazing people.

Forward

Before I was diagnosed with breast cancer at 38, with three children under the age of six, I was passionate about writing and singing. And afterwards. But during, I sank low. I refused to think I was depressed, cared only for my tiny children, and rejected professional help and support groups alike. I stopped singing and writing, which for me is akin to not breathing. I'm a "doer", so friends and family were very worried as I withdrew to a solitary place, full of fear and anxiety.

One dark day after what was supposed to be my "last" chemo treatment, I spotted a brilliant buoy floating my way, cast by Nancy Morgan, Director of Arts & Humanities Program at Georgetown Lombardi Comprehensive Cancer Center. We met when a wonderful social worker named Tara Heery introduced us. When I learned Nancy used writing to help patients, I mentioned tentatively that I wrote poetry, and she dared me to show her. I took the risk, sent her a poem, and she wanted more. It was just what I needed—validation at a time when there was little left of myself. Nancy reached out, grabbed me and the poems, and was positively excited about my idea to create an anthology for patients called "Lombardi Voices", now in its fifth volume. It became my focus—I was not underneath it; instead, I was forming and guiding it, with Nancy, for myself and for others. I felt the fog lifting. And I kept writing.

The writings herein span four years and this book has been dwelling in the shadows of my mind for a long time. My great hope is to connect with readers, one at a time, as they make their way through painful days that also are the very life they crave. Through writing and the arts, we can leave a trail of who we are.

My writings are a spider's thread attaching me to my family and friends forever; they will never have to wonder how I felt, they will know, and for that, I am thankful.

Who

It's anybody's guess
She was tired of her long hair
She's unconventional
She's an artist
She likes a buzz cut
She's a lesbian
She's from New York City
She's a movie star
She's cool
She has cancer
Depends who's looking

Underworld

Infusion

it's just a room, well, rooms really
where people spend some hours
getting their treatments, you know,
their infusions
sounds lovely, like peppermint tea served
in a golden tea cup with butter cookies to dip
like a day spent soaking delicate toes in
foamed perfumed water, painted the perfect color
my infusion begins when I suck in frosted air
that slaps my face
and sends me home to little arms.

AC

Thinking crazy thoughts
about time and me and life
I waited for the grey to clear
and bring tomorrow near

It was slower than molasses
Longer than a race
Uglier than garlic
And more tiring than the grave

And when I saw my shadowed head
Rise up from the pain
My only thought:
Road kill was my name.

Nadir

When I start writing, will it be the opening of a black ironic work that drills into my consciousness like a bore? Or will it be a paragraph of intense suffering and self-pity that unravels into philosophical drivel? Nothing could prepare me for this moment in life and nothing will ever be the same. Or maybe it's all the same except for me, yes, just for me and a slimy residue on my family. That's all. A look of "oh dear", "how can I help", a meal on the doorstep in a bright straw picnic basket bringing the suggestion of grassy meadows and sunshine. Calls, cards, food, flowers. Thank God it's not me. How lucky I am. I should appreciate every day. Resolve, resolve, promise.

And here I am, having banished myself to the basement, where I sleep in the reclining chair like a punished dog, howling to get out, biting and scratching to get upstairs, where I belong. Here I sleep, sitting up, two pillows, no, one pillow, twinging pain on my right, pulsing pain on my left. Barely able to type, breathe, laugh, see the light somewhere, waiting for me, or maybe not.

I have lost the desire to take care of my own children. Now I know I am dispensable, even to the only ones I loved. I couldn't bear to tell them, haunted for weeks by the potential of their faces, their tears, their souls. I told, I cried, I left, I came back. They were fine. They didn't fall apart, miss school, they stayed children and did what they do. So my father was right, they don't need me as much as I thought they did. How generous to be proven right, so thoughtful to relieve me of worries. How easy to be rendered useless. Thanks, from the bottom of my heart. Because now, I no longer have to worry about what would happen; I know. All my hard work will march forward with or without me.

So I'm pissed, with nowhere to fling my anger except upon myself, my husband and the absence of a higher reason. From mommy to monster, from loving to empty, from happy to horrified, here I am. The new me, the bruised breastless me, the newer, better model. And with chemotherapy, I'll be a wonder. And when my ovaries are removed and my hormones dry up, I'll be perfect. A perfect mess. A perfect lonely person whose husband will find greener pastures, because I am too angry, too mean, too bitter, too horrible to bear. A perfectly sad me. A me I never dreamed would come from that laughing portrait upstairs in my daughter's room. A me that has a wrinkled brow, tired eyes, tears, no strength, no hugs, no kisses, nothing soft, nothing. Nothing at all to give beyond weariness.

Is this it? Is this my forever? Is this all I get? Isn't there much more? How much? Why doesn't anyone tell me? Damn it, what have I done? The silence is nothing, there is no reason. It just is. And I have to come to terms with nothing and make something out of it, or just exist there.

So please, tell me how depressed I am. That everything will be all right. That I'm lucky. Go ahead and tell me how everyone needs me so much, how things will get better. Let everyone feel better by helping me. I wish I were the one leaving food on the doorstep and then driving home feeling appreciative, for a moment not taking things for granted, promising to be a better mother, wife and person. I'd like to be the one sending flowers, cards and visiting. So much better to be the visitor than the visited.

Chair

Sitting in the chair
Effortlessly as poison greets
Formerly pristine veins
Sitting, waiting for hours to pass
To get the stuff in and out
In to do the work
Out to feel better
Clear, red, clear
And then just a bruised arm
Itchy head, tired of sitting legs
Ok, now four days of such awful exhaustion
This is what dying must feel like
It couldn't be worse so tomorrow will be better
And it is. No resting, no naps
Back to life for two weeks, until the next time
I sit in the chair

New Day, No Breast

new day, no breast
no shirts, no rest,
no drain, big squishy lump
so ugly, so gone, so sad
I hear cicadas charged with the purpose of living
mating dying
din in my ears, I can't hear it today, maybe tomorrow

life as a unibreast
woman with one breast missing
person with one breast still there
same, different
defined just as much by what isn't as what is
scars remind, absence reminds
get on with the business of living
with a little less than before

It's not supposed to matter
but it does
a lot
they tell me I am not my breast
they tell me I'll get used to it
they tell me I'll get over it
they tell me the most important thing is to live
they're all right
and wrong

with no promises, no reassurances,
sometimes a loss is just that
Meaninglessly Simple
Infinitesimally Complete
Resolutely Absolute.

Staring

It's not easy to sit here without staring
To want to know why she's here
So guant, I see them, men and women
Young, in wheelchairs
Taking small laborious steps
Hollowed cheeks
Tired, gone eyes
Tired, can't cook
Tired, carries a cane
Who is the patient?
Whose child is that?
She's going to the 7th floor, to the infusion room
I want to smile at her but a wall of solid grief and
strength pushes outward
No one can approach the fortress I've inside, no one
I wave at my friends
Feeling up for a moment
Anxious
Waiting for the sword

Stiff Hairs

Straight like soldiers, waiting for orders
Jabbing at both ends into hats and scalp
Receding from my hairline
Just enough to remember, not enough to make a difference

flying nun hats with an ear flap to hide what's missing
swoop-over-one-eye hats with the allure of hair tucked up
down on the farm bandanas that someone thinks are sexy
        but remind me of pancakes
tight beanie hip hop hats of a rebellious teenager
snug chic knotted hats, a leather one, of a European woman
        who wore it proudly
flowing scarves not quite secured tightly, threatening to sail off
elasticized oblong turbans sitting crookedly on a round head
coiffed tilted itchy wig

Hatless
Hairless
Waiting for orders
To march back up there and put the uniform back on

Searching

I find myself in front of the mirror
Fifty times a day
My nose pressed up against the glass
Eyes turned upwards
Head tilted this way and that
"What are you doing now?"
"Just looking"
Yes, it's there, I think
For sure, from a distance there's a brown shadow
Up close, tiny blond fuzz
My hand sneaks up and runs along the top, the sides, the back
Were they there all along? Are they new?
Why did I think it would take a couple of days, weeks?
I keep searching
And looking
And waiting
And wondering why it's so urgent
To see something new

True Friend

She tells me I'm beautiful when I look at her
with red eyes and a fuzz covered hat
She tells me I look great for someone going through
what I'm going through
She tells me that I'm amazing for continuing to work
through near complete exhaustion
She picks up my daughter from school and casually
drops off food to taste
She calls me up each day to see how I am feeling
and knows how to cheer me up
She treats me like the normal person I used to be
unusual
my friend

Waiting

After all this, more?
Looking down I see worry in my doctor's eyes
Nine stitches later I go home
My husband thinks it will be ok
My father says he's pretty sure it will be ok
It doesn't matter
It is what it is
So I wait

Finished

So I'm "done"
and all that goes with it
Leaving me suspended
yeah, I know, no one knows for sure
I could be hit by a car
but how to live with plans that scream hubris
or without plans that cry of hopelessness
It takes time, they say
Give it to me, I demand

Lead Shot

It's a weight that starts in my stomach and loads into my head
As I lay in the dark
As I lay to gather strength for the next day and make my way back
    to good days
I see the last year as if from the moon
Disbelief, how could every single month for 16 months
Be remembered by a biopsy, a test, an appointment or several
Surgery, scars, asymmetry, baldness, sadness, fear, pain
Everyone calls it a nightmare
It's my life, my life, I need to find my life
And throw this curse off my back
Knowing that no matter how hard I try
It's not up to me
I still don't believe I have breast cancer
I still can't believe I have breast cancer
I still can't accept that my life might be much shorter
    than I ever anticipated
How I long for the days when I could take one minute for granted
That's gone now
I venture out with just a cap and go between rage and pride
I'm pissed people are looking at me and I'm pissed that they're
    looking away
I'm sick of being uncomfortable for other's sake
But for my own, too
My daughter is embarrassed by my scalp
I tell her to always hold her head high and be proud no matter what
But I cry and cry
Silently wishing to go home and curl up alone
Still trying to get a grip, to grasp at a truth
That I don't want to ever see or hear or think

Sweet Ambrosia

Mother-Daughter Lunch

Yesterday, I had a lovely morning with my six-year old daughter, Sophie. It was quite unexpected. While my husband took the boys to baseball, Sophie and I went to get a quick trim, which she only agrees to twice a year. She came with me to get a pedicure and sat patiently while my toes turned a beautiful shade of pink she chose for me. We went to the barrette store and then decided to have lunch at a Thai restaurant, where we like to go when there are no fussy food boys around.

The restaurant was empty except for a women sitting alone near the window next to us. She had a turban on her head and was knitting something spectacular and golden. I focused on Sophie and we ordered, sharing fried tofu and vegetarian pad thai. I wanted to just enjoy lunch, as the mother of a beautiful little girl, without getting caught up in that other stuff. But my eyes kept slipping past Sophie time after time.

I tried, I really tried, but I couldn't do it.

Is she all alone? How can I let her know I was sitting in her seat, carefully sipping soup under a wig not long ago? How can I show her that although I look normal, I'm not? And will that make her feel better? Or does she want forget for a while and just eat? Does she see me looking at her hat and think I am uncomfortable? How can I make sure she doesn't misinterpret my staring for fear, rather than for support? I wished I had a secret signal.

We finished our meal. As we waited for the bill, I told the woman that her knitting was beautiful, and that last year, at the Lombardi Cancer Center, where I was a patient, there was a knit-in, with the most beautiful streamers of color and texture strung from the stairs. I told her that I used to go with my grandmother to pick wool and wished I could knit, but never did learn. Too impatient, even when I was stuck at home during the tired months.

She smiled and as we talked her face grew lighter. I said goodbye. I cried all the way home. I won't hesitate next time. I'll remember that being connected by the thinnest string is a thousand times better than being alone.

Boxed In

one lies at my head
his body curling along the pillow towards me
the other clutches my left
her warm palms clasping mine
my sunshine's head finds the right place on my chest
and his tiny fingers play with my nose
the furry fourth one lies at my feet
When I came home for the first time
I slept alone, never believing I would be able to feel again
a tiny head on my surgically removed chest
or a slight hand pressed to my wet cheek
I absorb warmth from all sides until I fall asleep

Breathing

TO SOPHIE

Breathing, in and out, in and out
Raspy at times, smooth at others
She sprawls there, arms and legs akimbo
Heart shaped mouth in a relaxed O
Breathing, in and out, in and out
Brown hair decorating her pink pillow
Her feet making a V on the butterfly sheets
Suddenly turning over to reveal one perfect cheek
I kiss her
Her melody sings me to sleep
Breathing in and out, in and out

Superhero

TO BENJAMIN

On sweet bird song days like today,
I wonder if the inevitable would be better
than waiting for the executioner to tap me
or just cast his shadow on the door
"Is it that cancer thing?" my son asks.
"When is it going to be over?"
innocent unconscious wisdom
he is eight
not able to hug anyone today as I wait
to change back from radioactive spider woman
to mommy
a whole day I missed
one whole precious irreplaceable day

Skin

TO BENJAMIN

Fringed emerald eyes peer at me above a freshly-browned nose
Red athletic shorts hastily pulled on, shirt barely stretched over his frame
We race through minutes getting shoes, bagels, juice, lunch ready
     and hop into the traffic to get there in time
He jumps out of the car, looks back with a half-smile
"Bye, mom" as I drive away, looking for the glint of his soles
     in the rear-view mirror
Getting my things done is just a pretext for returning early
I watch from a distance, balls flying, attention focused
Under the steamy haze
That covers the field
He sees me
I see him
When the inning is over, he runs to me
and slips his hand into mine

Girl Child

TO SOPHIE

she's slightly mysterious, slightly whimsical
blue fringed eyes, delicate pointed nose
heart shaped mouth with pearly teeth
thin legs and arms
so beautiful, so generous, so tough, so determined
little snuggler, mouthfuls of kisses
"I want mama" she cries
my heart cracks a little more
she holds it together for me, my little angel

Leaving

TO BENJAMIN

Grey morning
So early in the day
He starts his journey without me
How will I know where he is, where he goes
He is so small
The path has been long and hard
But I still wish I had it to do over again,
Again and again, forever
I desperately want to pull him back
And want him to go
Stong and safe
I will try to keep my heart together today
As I feel him going, going

Delicious Babe

TO ZACHARY

His eyes float up to mine
His wide smile closes upon my mouth
Cool cheek presses against my warm one
Curly uncut hair
Tiny fat tush
Little fast leggies
My baby boy

Baby Z

TO ZACHARY

On your second birthday
You stare with deep blue long-fringed eyes
Pouting your delicious lower lip just like your daddy's
Feared lost after the first cut, now hints of curls again
Little tiny thin-at-the-ankles legs that run with such speed
Ten toes to eat several times a day
"tummy make, mommy, tummy make" means we need to snuggle
"uppy" and "bumbum boderin' me" and "I wub you"
and "own self" and "firsty"
and so many more amazing words streaming forth
from under your perfect nose
So familiar, so unique
I would gaze at you forever if you'd let me
But already, you're pulling ahead, doing more and more
I want to cling to the fleetingness of soft skin and tickles
But here comes two, and I know it will be a fantastic adventure
So I let go and wait to see the wonders that you will show me

For Jonathan

It's not as if we haven't walked to the ends of the earth and back, hand in hand, through ashes and flowered gardens;

It's not as if we haven't noticed that exhausted days end and the sun comes up every morning;

It's not as if we haven't gazed at our beautiful children wondering how they came to be yet not remembering a time without them;

It's not as if we haven't wept at sadness whittling away solidity and threatening to whisk away all things cherished in a heart beat;

It's not as if we haven't feared the worst and worried about things we couldn't know yet hoped for precisely the opposite;

And yet, my dearest Jonathan, we have come through on the other side, still hand in hand, and now I am certain, absolutely certain, that nothing will ever separate us, not time, not night, not days, not darkness.

I love you for transforming my dreams into life.

Grace

TO CYNTHIA AND MADELINE

Burnished mahagony graces the foyer
and leans against cool walls and pastel carpets
pictures framed by ingenious string that surrounds and structures
bright light saunters in to say hello and leaves a shining residue
on the faces of her beautiful children
who love me instantly when I arrive and let me peek into their
world of soccer and piano and food and round tables
We run together through pink balloons
hand in hand to the finish line
accelerating with growing smiles
"You can do it, Aunt Lisa"

Once, maybe twice, in a life
a soul is born with the sensitivity and pureness of a dew drop
a tiny luminescent crystal
so able to peer deeply into another's spirit
otherworldly knowing more than is possible
so careful not to tread
beyond a fairy's wings
so bright and warmly compassionate
she spurs me on
to do better than I believe I can
she holds my hand and pulls me
towards the finish line

Group Mentality

When I am surrounded by pink and white shirts
I'm not sure how I feel
I'm happy that I'm among those present but
Feel strongly the absence of others
Who should be here, too
We three sisters are still here, we sisters three
And we have run together to prove it
Moving forward
At the finish, I meet my sister's friend who isn't moving with us
She's there but I am frightened by her face
A face I recognize as identical to mine not long ago
With no eyebrows looking out from under a hat
But hers is the face of a future I hope I'll never wear
I feel the sheer will of her spirit that keeps her standing
And understand that as long as she stands, she has hope
Of belonging to our group, which is better than not belonging
The pink shirts scare me and comfort me
I guess that's why I came

Creation

TO JESSICA AND JULIA

Finally, I see
where she lives
what she has created
from ashes she thought would last forever
so full of grace, so carefully chosen
it's perfect
and whole and bright
and full of promise and comfort
A place of belonging and color
encouraging great solitude in a garden of choices
illuminated by a brilliant sparkle of a child
wafer-thin and curly
a constant reminder of life's endless possibility

Renewal

Chic

Today I look good
Dare I say "hot"?
For the first time in two years
I have a great haircut, actually, I have hair
Chic, I'd say
The poncho from Utah thrown over my shoulders
Draws compliments
And my brown suede boots are cool
Tortoise shell sunglasses top it off
When I walk alone through the airport
On my special trip to see my sisters
Men look, women glance
Now I remember how good I can feel
Hair rocks

The Lesson

He wears dark sunglasses
and carries three children around his neck
giving lessons interrupted by kisses
He loves the water, he loves them
His powerful arms hold them up
Carefully teaching the things
He learned when his mother came to cheer
So quiet, so kind, so gentle

Rhythm

steel drums beat from hidden speakers
oiled skins order pina coladas
blond brown straight curly ponytails everywhere
accented by vanishing suits
and sunburned children
short hairs catch the breeze and greet inquiring eyes
funky sunglasses, lipstick, hoop earrings, new pants, new breasts, new shirt
who cares
feeling good

Wishes

There's a wishing fountain beneath the balcony
That looks at the frothy ocean beyond spiny palm leaves
And it's a full of coins
I don't have a penny to toss
But I make a wish anyway
Piggybacked on everyone else's
Under the orange moon
As I walk back to put my three children to sleep
And perhaps lean into my husband's arms for a moment
I make a wish
There used to be so many
Now I just want the chance to enjoy just one
The orange moon's promise is beautiful
I want to gaze at it for as long as I can

Celadon Vase

TO GARY GENETTI

Pale moon luminescence graduates into celadon sky
Graced by silhouetted wing beak and stem
Etched from carbon skin
Poised on floating caps of stalks and straw
Tilted heads playfully provoking
Under eastern light
I fall in love over and over
Wondering at the creator of such
A tiny perfect world

Into the Next Stage

TO MY MOTHER

It's time to make a date with middle age
To arrange conveniently to have what's left of my youth
Surgically removed by a skilled surgeon
I'll make an appointment to meet him
And when I awake, I'll be old
In the next stage of life which, from here,
Means no more children or hopes of them
Even though I know that's gone anyway
Perhaps I'll lose my voice, which I have just learned to let fly
Perhaps I'll feel tired, even through I just emerged
From post-chemo exhaustion
Perhaps I'll be cranky or dried up or prune-like
I'll never be so young again as I am now
And that is hard to make an appointment to ensure
So into the next stage,
Where at least I'll have a better chance of living
Far from my youth with all its unknown threats
To a safer place with fewer worries and farther from pain
Closer to my mother who gradually entered her next stage
Away from youth toward the unknown
Reluctantly, hand in hand, but still walking forward
Eager to see what's around the bend

Dinner with Friends

working, writing, accounting for
everything I've done in the last year
for a moment, I stop thinking about myself
and anticipate dinner with friends
in a warm place with smiles and chatter
and food, good food
connecting with souls and wild spirits
and intelligence and hearts
makes life worthwhile
friends worn comfortable with familiar looks
and words and ways of thinking
to just exist in the essence of time
is a luxury seldom permitted
I can't wait for dinner tonight
made by someone else in a colorful kitchen
behind a wall, perhaps partially exposed,
for my friends and me

Vivi's Kitchen

TO AVIVA

Yesterday, I went back
to Vivis' kitchen
where we cooked side by side
talking about food and recipes and ideas
mixing ricotta and broccoli and sauce
and laughing about "mixed green salad and a crusty loaf of bread"
We had each one child and a meeting of the minds
and when we were done we had created something
we both would remember
had started us on a journey that now,
seven years later, almost eight
seems like seconds
We roasted, we grilled, we baked, we toasted
watching our bucket heads run around and bang the toilet lids
and get covered with chocolate pudding
Now we read cookbooks, and talk and talk and talk
about things we never dreamed we'd talk of
and in the future,
we'll talk about things we never dream we'll talk of
all the while, roasting, grilling, baking and toasting
to many more

Demons

Subconscious

Another day, another test
Middle of the night MRI
Not that I'm worried
Although I do feel a new lump
Chances are slim that I'd have a new cancer
In the other breast that I had removed
But still, shit happens
The nurse called the doctor on the plane who said
It was ok to tell me the news was good
"Benign" enhancement doesn't sound good at first listen
"Suspicious" enhancement is worse for sure,
And since I've heard that before
I'll go with the former today
Enjoy my race tomorrow
And worry about it constantly

Scare

The dining room table stretches to the picture window
Painted with swaths of greenery
For the first time in months, it is raining
The heavens opened just as I descended to the dark bottom
A place I hate to visit and fear remembering
Sticky pungent walls of slime pull me down
The light only a pinprick above
I remember I was just up there a few days ago
Then my mind clouded and argued and thought
And took me back into the hole
Living with a monster inside that I can't see or feel
Who lurks amid my very soul and shows itself
Whenever it sniffs uncertainty in the air
How do I live with the beast within
In the light and shadows of such a beautiful life

Drizzle

Tears stream down my cheeks
I'm not sure why they're coming now
"Does it seem like a long time ago?" a friend asks
A mist covers my eyes briefly, yes and no
Half in, half out
Unwilling to desert, unable to abandon
Thinking and thinking, trapped in foggy time
Forced to recall and put into order
At lunch, on the phone, on e-mail
Friends, friends of friends, strangers
Tonight, my son declares he wanted to be with his friends
Tonight, the years fly in my face
Tonight is a night I dreamed I would have
If I lived which is all I wanted
My heart stings and I don't know
Whether I am supposed to laugh or cry
Time is a cruel companion, either way

Gone

In all the trees and bushes, I had never seen a nest
Strange, given how the whortle of a mourning dove told me
    this was home
But in spite of the activity, no nest
So I walked outside to figure which branches I could trim
From the Japanese maple obscuring my kitchen sink view
Peered up and saw the woven basket
Built right in front of my very eyes
Smooth lacquered empty walls
Was I too late? It was June, after all
But I watched as I cooked and
The two came together on the flagstone wall
Creating four perfect blue eggs to decorate the floor
Mama sat
I cracked open the window and sang to mama
She sang back
And sat
Through wind and storms and barbeques and my birthday
First one pink hairless beak, then three more
We'd drag over the chair on the deck, gently pull over the branch
And peek in
"Don't leave a scent," I warned
Mama fed them all day, and warmed them at night
Papa helped, too, bringing worms and critters for hungry mouths
Their wide beaks popped over the edge of the nest
Peeping, cheeping and wobbling
I made fish for dinner on the new grill
In the morning the tree was empty
I gasped and ran
birds screaming and flapping and crying
circling and searching

Time Machine

In a flash of recognition
Twenty-five years vanish and reveal
A sixteen year old girl with beauty, allure
Whose best friend that summer is a boy
Who she knows is just like the person she'll marry
Dark haired, awkward, sweet
Panic rises in her throat
Self-conscious to the cellular level
He's handsome, filled out, manly
She wishes her hair were down
That she were twenty pounds thinner
That she was still the girl
But she laughs and is excited
He throws out that she broke his heart
She wishes she could wipe off the residue of reality
And go back
For just another minute

Elizabeth and Me

TO ELIZABETH EDWARDS

She smiles and looks fine
She presses forward as planned
Analysis, commentary follow
Carefully chosen words cast in the best light
Followed by serious medical analysis
With statistics and facts undercutting the presentation

From her recurrence are born millions of particles of fear
Spewed forth in a split second
Spilling out, spurring phone calls and e-mails
Tremors give way to complete unrest
A solidarity of knowing and worrying
And wishing there was no one to read about

We sister soldiers move forward
Because to do otherwise is to die prematurely
In waiting comes confession
That we are only fleeting on this hallowed ground
Where breath and light and arms vanish
Without permission or desire

What we are in our moments is only known
By the sum of our completed time
Tallied at the final second
And written as such

At the end of each day, I wonder whether
The note taker penned anything additional to the final lines
That will codify my existence
But promise to wake up on the next sun's beam
Reassured that when that happens, I will be in a tangle of love
For at least one more day

Tornado

Out the window of my friend's house
(She is not much of a friend anymore)
I spot a black funnel cloud
Far enough away that there is time to run
Close enough that there isn't much time before it's too late
It just hangs there, inching closer, while I scream
And gather my children
We run to the basement but it's not a basement
It's a regular floor with windows
They get away with my husband on his scooter
It's raining
They can't all ride, some fall off, I watch them leave
Unable to escape the tornado that both is and isn't coming
It's waiting for me
It hovers, sometimes moving closer, then farther away
Maybe safe, maybe not
All I can do is hope and pray that it won't touch down
And destroy what's left

The Rapid River

TO NANCY MORGAN

Ambivalent hues of muddy flow interrupted by rusted cans,
Moldy sticks and an occasional boot.
Sometimes, when the sky blues after rain
You can see a hint of transparency.

Light squares bounce on the gentle flow,
Rising and falling in a silent boat's wake.

Tales of nighttime rowdiness,
Silent kisses and historic crossings,
Rich loam and homelessness,
Golden sludge that remembers.

Constant waters keep great stories
Of crossings, spring times and drowning.

It leaves me at the door of infinity,
For I know it will take me
Down time's road
Even if I try to swim back.

Ladies Lunch

When I was feeling stronger than I had in a while, I invited 12 friends to lunch. Lunch is my favorite meal, it's the one my grandmother made for me when I was growing up: soup, cottage cheese and sour cream with fruit, triscuits, homemade cookies or pie. Sometimes we ate on the porch, sometimes at the table looking over the field, with bird feeders strung on trees all around us. My grandfather would read the paper or watch his tiny black and white t.v., while my grandmother served.

Dinner parties are stressful, with children running around, and always the quest for perfection. My ladies luncheon was a better idea. I could have it during school hours, prepare it in the morning and relax. The day before, I bought all the ingredients and went to a local consignment store. I picked out 12 china plates of different designs. I stopped at the flower store and found 12 tiny potted flower plants. Driving home with my treasures, I delighted in planning the next three hours.

My menu was solid: open faced brie, fig preserve and carmelized onion sandwiches on baguettes; a spinach salad with goat cheese, dried cranberries and toasted almonds; roasted sweet potato and apple soup; and chocolate mousse with all the fresh berries I could find.

Peering down my long dining room table, I went to work, setting the table with all the treasures and then putting the finishing touches on the food.

One by one, my 12 friends came. Some I had not known before cancer; some I had known but not well; others were old friends. They had all helped me through a hard time and now I could properly thank them.

We feasted and talked and drank. And then they left, unique plate and plant in hand, with hugs and kisses. I cleaned up and knew I had turned the corner.

Afterwords

Details

When I meet someone with breast cancer, sometimes the conversation starts with questions about what happened. We each relate and distance ourselves with the details, sometimes feeling safer, sometimes not.

I was diagnosed in September 2003 with breast cancer. At the time, I was 38 and had a six-year old son, a four-year old daughter and a one-year old son. A year before, my youngest sister had been diagnosed with breast cancer. We had no family history to warn us, so I am certain that my sister's ability to look fear in the eye and listen to her inner voice saved my life.

After a double mastectomy with reconstruction, I did 4 rounds of AC which caused me to descend into depression—I felt as though I barely escaped. And seemingly for nothing, since soon after, two more small tumors were found, and I ended up having a total of eight surgeries and another round of chemo just as my hair was starting to look decent. I had my ovaries removed, entered menopause officially, and elected to have DIEP flap surgery which was ten hours long. Sometimes, I cannot believe I survived the surgeries alone.

What was the hardest part? Telling my children and holding my broken heart together as they cried and worried and wondered and I had to tell them about all the hope while just underneath not believing any of it; watching my exhausted husband take care of three children and me, go to work, and deal with the distant memory of being seven when his mother fought breast cancer, mourning her death which came only a year before my diagnosis; seeing my parents eyes look at me and through me with fear and denial; realizing it is a fight, it never goes away, and that you can lose whether you fight or not.

My sister is doing well. I am doing well. We both know that we are doing well today, and that there are no guarantees about tomorrow. So we live for today and hope that tomorrow will be as bright as the day just passed.

About the Author

Lisa Flaxman graduated from Brown University (1987) and Georgetown University Law Center (1994), and is a fully recovered lawyer. Currently, Ms. Flaxman is Founder and CEO of musiKids® (www.musikids.com), an early child-hood music education company dedicated to teaching music to infants-five year olds. Through musiKids, she publishes musiKonnections, a monthly e-newsletter linking the community. Ms. Flaxman serves as Executive Director of musiKares, a public campaign she started to collect and recycle CDs by donating them to hospitals to help relieve patient anxiety, for which she was awarded Maryland Top Innovator of 2007 (Daily Record). In recognition of her leadership and community involvement, Ms. Flaxman was chosen as one of Maryland's Top 100 Women (May 2007) and received the first Women Business Owners of Montgomery County Sapphire Award (October 2006). Ms. Flaxman enjoys mentoring women entrepreneurs and is co-Founder of mompreneurcoach.com and Women's Entrepreneur Group (WEG). She is a board member of Center for Inspired Teaching and Sinai House, a full-service transitional house in DC, and volunteers many hours a year to community and educational outreach initiatives. Ms. Flaxman is co-author with Aviva Goldfarb of the cookbook Peanut Butter Stew and Couscous, Too, and a frequent contributor to The Six O'Clock Scramble e-newsletter (www.thescramble.com). She is Editor of Lombardi Voices, a poetry anthology of patient writings published semi-annually by Georgetown Lombardi Comprehensive Cancer Center's Arts & Humanities Program. Ms. Flaxman has published articles on early childhood music and has been featured in numerous articles and on local and national television and radio programs discussing breast cancer and the arts, musiKares, early childhood music education, and being a "mompreneur". Ms. Flaxman is a coloratura soprano and sings a wide-range of opera, art song, musical theatre, folk and children's world music. Ms. Flaxman lives with her husband, Jonathan Martel, three children, Benjamin (10), Sophie (8) and Zachary (5), and her dog, Boo, in Chevy Chase, MD. She loves to sing loudly in the kitchen while cooking.

Debunking Myths

No one is too young to get breast cancer. My sister was 28, I was 38. It's not an old woman's disease.

Don't talk yourself into thinking you are safe just because it doesn't run in your family.

Don't stick your head in the sand—early detection and diagnosis can save your life. Be your own best friend and fiercest advocate.

A breast cancer lump does not go away if you ignore it.

Breast cancer can be passed down from the father's side, as well as the mother's.

Do not visit chat rooms.

Two good websites: YoungSurvival.org and breastcancer.org.

Get a mammogram at age 35; if you have a family history of breast cancer or other reason for concern, insist on an MRI.

If you feel something is wrong, don't let anyone convince you otherwise. Get a second opinion. Then a third.

Don't wait for this stage to pass—live in the moment, don't look to far ahead.

Don't go it alone—get professional help; it's very lonely and people who have never been depressed can fall into it.

Let friends help even if you don't want them to—you'll get a chance to give back in some way.

When the fear gets the best of you, think "tomorrow may be a better day" and don't give away hope.

Even a dark, sardonic sense of humor is better than none at all.